a message from terry brooks

Dear Readers,

Welcome to a new Shannara adventure and a grand experiment. *Dark Wraith of Shannara* is both a completely new story and my first graphic novel. I was a little nervous about the idea of a graphic novel at first, worried that it would not live up to your expectations—not to mention my own. But the people at Del Rey felt that this was the right time to give it a try, and I must say after viewing the finished product that they were right.

It was a very deliberate decision to come up with something new for readers. A rehash of any existing Shannara story just didn't seem enough for this new format. A fresh story was needed, and I had been thinking about doing something more with Jair Ohmsford and Garet Jax ever since publication of the novella "Indomitable" a few years back. There was more to explore about their relationship, and the ambiguity regarding the fates of brother and sister Jair and Brin Ohmsford could stand a little better resolution. Since I didn't expect to go back into that time period any time soon, *Dark Wraith* seemed a good place to make that happen.

Hopefully, you will agree. No introduction in the form of previous Shannara stories is needed to read this book. As with much of my work, you can pretty much begin anywhere. Generational sagas allow for that. If there is enough interest, we'll think about doing another one. We keep trying to find new ways to satisfy the demand for fresh stories, and this is the latest.

Much good reading always. It's still the best escape we have.

BY TERRY BROOKS

DARK WRAITH OF
SHANNARA

TERRY BROOKS

illustrated by edwin david

adapted by robert place napton

BALLANTINE BOOKS * NEW YORK

A Del Rey Trade Paperback Original

Published in the United States by Del Rey Books, an imprint of The Random House Publishing Group, a division of Random House, Inc., New York.

ISBN: 978-0-7394-9406-6

Printed in the United States of America

Adapter: Robert Place Napton
Inker: Dennis Crisostomo
Toner: Brian Buccellato
Lettering: Dana Hayward

contents

PROLOGUE

the Great Wars have come and gone, and a world much like our own has succumbed to an armageddon of its own making.

A thousand years have passed. Now science—once thought to hold all the secrets of the universe—has been replaced by a new power with an arcane name . . . magic.

Using this power, new races of Druids, Men, Dwarfs, Trolls, Gnomes, and Elves have struggled to bring a lasting order to the new world. New heroes have emerged to meet the challenge, and new legends have been born.

In the tale known as The Sword of Shannara, the Warlock Lord—once a wise Druid named Brona—succumbed to the dark magic of a dread tome known as the Ildatch and sought mastery over the other races. The Druid Allanon, protector of the Four Lands, conscripted Shea Ohmsford, descendant of the great Elven house of Shannara, to rediscover the mythic sword. After much adventure, the blade of truth was recovered, and it empowered Shea to vanquish the Warlock Lord once and for all.

In The Elfstones of Shannara, Allanon recruited Shea's grandson, Wil Ohmsford, and charged him with protecting the Elven girl Amberle on her quest to find the Bloodfire, which would save the Ellcrys tree and prevent imprisoned demons from overrunning the land. To complete his quest, Wil was forced to use the magic Elfstones—and in the process he permanently altered his own genetic makeup.

For the first time the Ohmsfords had magic in their blood, and Wil's daughter, Brin, and son, Jair, were born with the power of the wishsong. In The Wishsong of Shannara, Jair and Brin, like their father and great-grandfather before them, reluctantly embraced the Ohmsford heritage and answered the call of Allanon. The Ildatch—the very book of dark magic that had subverted the Warlock Lord—was working its twisted spell on his onetime mortal followers, transforming them into the Mord Wraiths, and only Brin and Jair could prevent the ruin of the world. The quest was a costly one, for Allanon was slain, and Jair lost many companions, including his most trusted, Weapons Master Garet Jax, in a fierce battle to save his sister, Brin, from becoming the Ildatch's dark minion. Ultimately, Brin used the wishsong to rend the Ildatch to shreds, burning it alive . . .

Though the price was high, Jair and Brin were successful. Evil was vanquished . . .

Or so they thought.

chapter 1

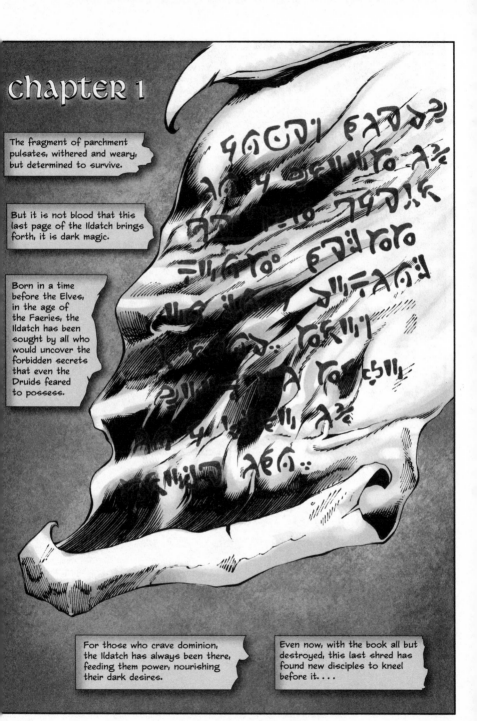

The fragment of parchment pulsates, withered and weary, but determined to survive.

But it is not blood that this last page of the Ildatch brings forth, it is dark magic.

Born in a time before the Elves, in the age of the Faeries, the Ildatch has been sought by all who would uncover the forbidden secrets that even the Druids feared to possess.

For those who crave dominion, the Ildatch has always been there, feeding them power, nourishing their dark desires.

Even now, with the book all but destroyed, this last shred has found new disciples to kneel before it. . . .

...awaiting the promise of its power.

They are the Mwellrets, acolytes of dark magic.

Someone walks among them, unseen and unheard.

An intruder who uses his magic song to trick their minds into believing he's invisible.

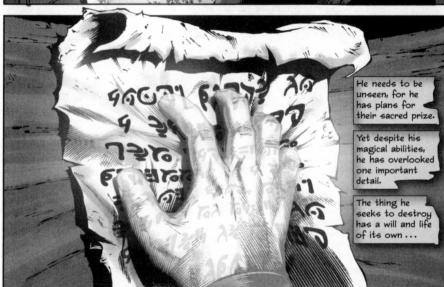

He needs to be unseen, for he has plans for their sacred prize.

Yet despite his magical abilities, he has overlooked one important detail.

The thing he seeks to destroy has a will and life of its own...

WHSSH!

The fragment lands with the sound of a boulder crashing to the ground, as if the parchment contains the weight of a thousand ages.

Still writhing in pain, Jair seeks the darkest shadows and uses the magic he was born with—the wishsong—to create the illusion that he has disappeared.

But it is too late.

We have guesstss!

Stay calm. Can't give myself away!

And don't look into those eyes!

Jair has succumbed to the Rets' hypnotic stare once before.

But there is a greater threat than the Rets' gaze—their *cleverness*—and a weapon more dangerous than the sharpest blade...

White powder.

The dust outlines everything it touches.

While the others swing blindly, seeking flesh to rive . . .

Steady. As long as they don't see me, there's still a chance.

... abandoning the illusion of invisibility for something more fearsome.

The Rets quickly
discover they are
battling little more
than colored vapor.

Ahr! It's
stuck!

And though he is horrified . . .

He is also exhilarated.

FHHT!

SHHT!

FHHT!

RRRAHH!

As quickly as it began, it ends.

There remains only the sound of fluttering torches...

But there is something else left in his wake.

JAIR...

...himself.

Though the image of who he used to be looks ghostly, as if fading in a muted wind...

DO SOMETHING, JAIR...

But the Ildatch...

...impaling it to the table amid the inferno.

He ignores the white heat...

Flesh and parchment burn...

Until he has no choice but to release his death grip...

ARRRGH!!!

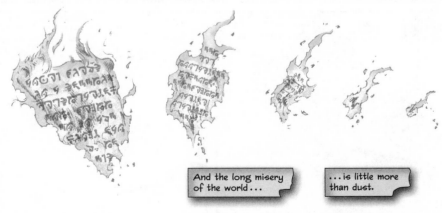

And the long misery of the world...

...is little more than dust.

Ahhh!

HURRY!

He walks through the image of the man he had been...

Feeling the weight of a lifetime lifted from his shoulders.

And watches the black-cloaked form...

...return to the land of the dead.

!

The same dream again!

Why?

The next day, Jair arrives in the Highlands of Leah...

...now the home of his sister, Brin Ohmsford.

Why didn't you *tell* me what happened when you destroyed the page?

I didn't want you to worry.

Besides, I wanted to forget about it.

Or try to, anyway.

But every night I relive it over and over. I can't figure out why.

Maybe it's a warning.

Of?

The danger of the magic. I've told you so many times, Jair, you just refuse to listen.

That's not fair, Brin. I was facing the Rets—in Dun Fee Aran—by myself.

I had to use the magic. There was no other way.

And *since* then?

I told you, nothing. Not once.

That's why I can't understand these nightmares.

Remember the old maple tree in our front yard.

When we were little, I sang...

And in the middle of summer you changed its leaves from green to autumn crimson...

Yes. The power to remake things has always been mine, Jair.

"Hard as you tried, you couldn't do the same thing."

"You could make things *appear* to happen..."

"But never once was it *real*."

Until now.

Maybe I've just grown up finally. Remember how you were always taller than me, and then that one summer I shot past you. Maybe it's like that.

Very well, if that's true, and your power *has* matured, then only you can stop it.

You have to give up the wishsong—for good.

You've been telling me that, Brin, but it's just not that easy.

◄ 27 ►

...on the western edge of the Duln Forests.

There he sojourns for the night.

"Promise me, Jair..."

"Never use the wishsong."

"Never risk losing yourself like that again."

AHHHHH!

....

Taking comfort in the simple beauty of the night sky, Jair's mind drifts inevitably to the memory of his transformation...

...of becoming someone else.

And it is this memory that tantalizes Jair as he finally surrenders to sleep.

Huh?!

YOU MUST FIND THEM, VALEMAN. RESCUE KIMBER AND COGLINE AND KEEP PARANOR SAFE. THE FATE OF THE FOUR LANDS DEPENDS UPON IT.

I can't, Allanon. Not this time.

I promised Brin—and myself. If I go after them, I'll end up using the magic again, we both know that.

I just can't take that chance.

WHEN I SOUGHT OUT YOUR SISTER THREE YEARS AGO, YOU WANTED TO ACCOMPANY HER TO MAELMORD.

I TOLD YOU THEN TO STAY IN SHADY VALE, BUT THERE WOULD BE ANOTHER TIME.

Promise me, never use the wishsong.

Help us, Jair.

THIS IS THAT TIME, VALEMAN.

As usual, you've left me with little choice, Allanon.

chapter 2

As day breaks, Jair does not continue his journey to Shady Vale. He turns away from the familiar path to home and heads northeast, skirting the edge of the Rainbow Lake...

...bartering for what he needs along the way.

Thank you, ma'am.

Safe roads ahead, my boy.

He rides eastward, through grasslands and wood, into an untamed land full of savage beauty...

...and beckoning memories.

When I was sent to save the land itself...

...by the King of the Silver River. He came to me as if from a dream.

I AM YOUR FRIEND, JUST AS I ONCE WAS FRIEND TO YOUR FATHER AND TO YOUR GREAT-GRANDFATHER BEFORE HIM...

He was that. He trusted me. And I trusted him.

I only wish he were here now.

I got a job coming up in a few days, tracking some poachers for farmers in the west lands. How about I drop by the Vale, we'll catch up then, have some of that awful soup you like.

I won't be there. I'm heading *east*.

Here.

Thanks.

Friends are in trouble. Kimber and Cogline. Remember them?

Sure, I remember them. Just like I remember all the others who died the last time I was fool enough to go with you. The Elf, the Dwarf, the Borderman... I remember them all—

"And Garet Jax, the Weapons Master, dead as a stone."

"That's a sight I won't soon forget."

Mwellrets have kidnapped Kimber and Cogline. They're going to use Cogline to find Paranor— the Druid's Keep.

Think of the Rets with Druid powers.

....

Don't care. Gulp!

I need you to track them. All I ask is that you help me find them. Then you can leave if you want to.

Gulp! Gulp! Gulp!

SLAM!

BELCH!

How many different times I got to say it, boy. I'm not interested in risking my neck again on some fool crusade to save the world.

So either buy me another drink or get going!

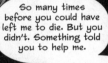

....

So many times before you could have left me to die. But you didn't. Something told you to help me.

Help me now, Slanter. I can't do this alone.

Many fear the Wolfsktaag, and with good reason. It is a place of old magic, populated by shape-shifting creatures whose origins are little more than legend.

Not necessarily an evil place, but certainly not a friendly one.

But it is the quickest route to Darklin Reach, home of Kimber and Cogline, where Slanter says they should begin their search.

Day's end is a welcome one as they leave the unrelenting wind of the passes behind for the warmth of the setting sun.

The next morning they find themselves in a wood rich with sights and smells familiar and reassuring, a wilderness largely unspoiled by civilization's trespass...

And towering above the red elms and giant pines is Hearthstone...

A natural rock formation shaped like a chimney, usually a welcomed sight...

But on this day, an eerie one.

Seems quieter here than I remember.

Mwellrets could still be slithering about. Keep your mind fixed on that.

A short time later...

Stop here, boy.

But that's the cottage up ahead.

Take a look at that.

Looks like clothing.

It is.

What's this smudge?

Blood.

This is where the Rets snatched them up. There's signs of a scuffle.

Come on, let's keep moving.

◄ 63 ►

RAAA.

What's got him riled?

What you said. *Kimber.*

Whisper—can you help us find Kimber?

Raaah!

He can find her, Slanter.

Boy, for all you know, he's tellin' ya he's hungry.

I don't think so.

Come on, Whisper, find Kimber.

You can't be serious?!

They follow the moor cat northeast, climbing another mountain trail, through the passes below Toffer Ridge...

This trail isn't much better than the Wolfsktaag—caves in these mountains are crawling with Spider Gnomes and it leads right into Olden Moor.

That's Werebeast country, in case you didn't know.

I know. Trust me, Slanter, Whisper knows what he's doing.

But do you, boy?

As Jair and Slanter's bickering echoes off the jagged rock that forms Toffer Ridge...

Even Slanter's keen senses fail to detect the presence of watchful eyes...

Spider Gnomes.

Creatures who are a mutation of his own kind, but more primitive and fierce...

But instead of attacking, the Spider Gnomes allow the travelers to pass into Olden Moor, a damp region shrouded in mist that perfectly hides the beings the Spider Gnomes worship as spirit creatures...

The Werebeasts.

I will.

I can smell the danger here, boy. Keep your wits about you.

The horses and Whisper are probably thirsty.

Think this is a good spot for a rest?

Good as any.

I'm tellin' ya, we'd been better off going back and letting me try to pick up their trail from the cottage.

I was so sure, but...

I don't see Ret tracks around here at all.

Maybe you're right.

Whisper, can you find Kimber? Are you leading us to her?

Well—we turning back?

Not yet.

Come on, Whisper, lead the way.

An hour passes, and the chilly dampness soaking through their clothes does little to improve Slanter's mood...

Nor does the sight of a cave where Whisper suddenly halts.

He seems to want us to go in there.

Werebeasts make their dens in caves just like this.

Stay with the horses, I'll take a look.

And get attacked standing out here by myself?

I'm going with you, boy.

He's worried about me, not himself. Good ol' Slanter.

"After that, we set out toward the mountains known as the Dragon's Teeth..."

"But I had found a broken fang in the Witch's prison..."

"I used it to cut my bonds... I wanted to help Grandfather..."

Run, girl, don't be a fool...

"I knew I had to get away first, then I could come back for him."

"I ran without looking back— deep into the moor."

"Then something came at me. But it wasn't a Ret..."

But instead I remembered this...

A fire shard!

Yes. Grandfather gave it to me years ago. He told me always to carry it—that its magic would one day protect me.

"I carried it around just to humor him, never thought I'd really need it."

"But as soon as the Werebeasts saw it, they fled in terror."

Shape-shifters can't get past fire shards—something about the light they don't take a liking to.

Shades, girl, you got some good luck.

It wasn't luck, it was Grandfather's foresight.

Either way, I'm grateful you're all right.

What I don't understand is how Whisper found you two so quickly?

I'll tell you everything later—first let's figure out how to get you out of here.

Anything's better than that cave.

You warm enough?

It's gonna be a bumpy ride, girl, you might have to grit your teeth some.

Yes, thank you, Jair.

Later . . .

This moor's endless. Are you sure we're going the right way?

Boy, do you want to trust my nose or yours? There isn't an inch of terrain I can't read. I know exactly where we are . . .

Trust me . . . we'll be out of here before you know it!

chapter 3

They move slowly over the rocky, wet marshland, careful not to jostle Kimber and make her injury worse, but mindful of the danger posed by Olden Moor and the urgent need to find Cogline.

Kimber suddenly feels eyes watching her.

She peers into the mist...

Her imagination and the thick miasma fuel her anxiety.

Even a gnarled branch becomes a threat...

But it's more than fear that's unsettling her nerves. She knows something is out there.

And she's not the only one...

Jair...

Hours later...
at Hearthstone...

I'll be happy to look after her, Valeman. Let's get her inside and I'll take a look at that leg.

We owe you a great debt.

Don't speak of it.

Shortly...

I still think Whisper should go with you. He could pick up Grandfather's scent in no time.

Whisper's got to let his wounds heal, just like you. Besides, on the way out of the moor, Slanter saw fresh Ret tracks leading toward the Dragon's Teeth.

Night comes, then another day, and by the next dusk they reach the opening through the Wolfsktaag Mountains known as the Pass of Jade...

Where Gnomes come twice a year to make offerings to appease the spirit gods that they believe reside throughout the ancient peaks.

Watch the shadows, boy.

WHO-HOO.
WHO-HOO.

Night enshrouds the Pass of Jade, bringing an air of foreboding.

Jax vaults toward the Koden, stunning it with his quickness...

In spite of its lumbering appearance, the Koden is by no means languid. It avoids the deathblow, and Jax maims rather than kills.

Driving the creature into a more savage frenzy.

It slashes with its remaining razor-sharp claws—a lesser man would have been riven.

But the Weapons Master is no ordinary man.

Uhhh...

...

Short swords still imbedded in its chest, the Koden begins to sway like a mighty tree that has been severed at its trunk...

Jair?!

But the only sound Slanter hears in reply is the final intake of rattled breath...

...and a deafening impact.

After a brief rest, Jair and Slanter head into the comforting expanse of the Rabb Plains, leaving behind the shadows of the Pass of Jade.

Tracks lead southeast, toward Varfleet. They're still a long way ahead of us.

Then let's get moving.

KA-THUD! KA-THUD!

Kennon Pass. It'll take us right through the Dragon's Teeth.

Later...

Have you ever been in this valley before?

Once or twice. More Ret tracks—and the old man's. They made him start walking from here.

SNIFF!
SNIFF!

Smoke—
that direction.
Let's go on foot.
Horses make too
much noise.

We're close,
don't make a
sound until
I tell you.

All right.

ꓕ1ꓕᄐ ꓵꓵᄂꓵꓵ
ᄂꓵꓵᄃꓵᄂ ꓵꓵꓵ ᄂꓵꓵ
ᄃꓵ ꓵᄂꓵᄐ.

We have to stop her!

Boy, what are you doing?

Running down there is going to get you killed, and Cogline will be no better off.

We have only one chance at this. It'll be nightfall soon, we can move down there easier then.

Rets are doing something.

She's probably close to getting what they want from him.

Take it easy, boy, we'll make our move soon as it's dark.

But Jair wonders if he can afford to wait for the dark...

chapter 4

Later...

HOO.

Mist is getting thicker.

It came from nowhere. What do you think it means?

Nothing good.

A thick fog, as if smoke billowing from the hearth of some unseen giant, begins to rise around them.

A faint thunder rumbles below her cold voice, which speaks the same chant over and over...

A wicked litany that always ends with the same word....

ᛏᚷᚾᛁᚱᚷᛊᛞ ᚷᚾᛁᛁᛚᚷᚾᛟᛒ... *Pa-ra-nor.*

Cogline is barely himself; his memory and essence are being siphoned into the black well of her being.

He is ready.

The Mwellrets tense with satisfaction. The moment they have schemed for is within their reach.

The indigenous population takes note of their passing ...

For the plateau that lies above ...

Is one they would not visit.

At last they arrive at their destination—a place with a dark history, where strange rituals were conducted by the first barbaric survivors of the Great Wars.

The mist swirls in response to Cogline's gesture.

In his youth he had been a Druid of great promise, but his love of old-world science put him at odds with the Druid Council. And rather than abandon his chemicals and theories, he left the sacred order before his teaching was complete.

Galaphile, Father of the Druids, hear me!

But that Druid power still resides deep within him...

And under the Witch's control, he calls upon it...

...to bring the Druid's Keep back from oblivion.

KRAKA-THOOM!

Old man's putting on quite a show.

It doesn't look good at all. Come on, Slanter, my plan will work.

I don't like it.

You have a better idea?

Yeah, something that's not going to get you killed and leave me with a bigger mess than the one we got!

Galaphile, First High Druid— hear me!

Bring forth Paranor!

KRAKA-THOOM!

Get back!

Jair sings . . .

But not the notes that brought about his transformation into Garet Jax.

Instead he sings as he did in his youth . . .

To instill in the minds of those around him . . .

The illusion of change . . .

I'd swear on my life you were a slime skin.

Now get moving, boy. No time to waste.

Jair moves quietly toward the group of Rets.

But they are too preoccupied to notice him.

A few Rets take notice of Jair as he passes, but the illusion works perfectly. To them he is simply one of their kind.

Galaphile, founder of Paranor, hear my call...

Bring forth the Druid's Keep...

The Witch, as if catching a faint scent in the wind, perceives the presence of magic other than Cogline's...

Restore it to this world!

KRAKA-THOOM!

?!

Galaphile, hear the call of your last son . . .

The presence she felt suddenly becomes apparent.

And though Jair moves quickly . . .

He is not quick enough.

The Witch's dark magic rolls over Jair like a torrent of water, drowning out the wishsong, washing away his illusory mask . . .

‹ 130 ›

Paranor...

A fragment of the great mountain upon which it used to reside hangs underneath it, a crumbling pedestal...

Above it, the ancient parapets and towers just as they were the day the great Druid Allanon and Jair's sister Brin oversaw Paranor's passing from this world.

And deep within the Keep, the Druid Library, filled with tomes of power.

The very chamber of knowledge the Rets intend to plunder.

...sliding backward...

Jair's boot scuffs against the ancient rock...

...until he feels nothing but air awaiting his next step.

KRAKA-THOOM!

I must do something...

chapter 5

As it looms ever closer, they all take notice . . .

Behind Jair, Paranor glides through the air like a colossal spectre . . .

Giving Jair the distraction he needs to sing . . .

. . . and give his power of illusion one last chance.

He surrenders completely to the Weapons Master's deadly precision...

...and indomitable strength.

He knows his enemies' moves even before they make them.

He glides like a phantom, countering before they can strike.

The battle is over before it begins.

He is invincible.

And he likes how it feels.

Behind them, quietly,
Paranor shudders...

But they are too fixated
on each other to notice.

The gate opens wide...
heaving forward with
a sudden vitality.

◄ 147 ►

For within the Keep there is a tower which hides a monstrous thing: a fathomless *pit*, impenetrably black, which guards the sanctuary of the Druids from all trespassers.

And Cogline, though under the Witch's control, has unknowingly awakened this power with his fervent chant...unleashing the fury of all the Druids who ever were.

And from within the pit of the tower, as the mist spreads outward like liquid fire, a hateful hiss rattles as though from an angry snake.

The hiss is so loud it masks the Witch's screams....

As she struggles to free herself from its inescapable grasp.

But Garet Jax hears another voice. Not the hissing pit, nor the witch's muffled screams, but a voice from somewhere inside of him: the Valeman he used to be ...

Telling him that this is a fight he cannot win, Weapons Master or not.

You don't mind if I ride with you a ways, do you, boy? I'm heading in the same direction anyway.

I don't have your nose...

...but I can smell a lie quick enough. Especially one of yours.

That so? Well, you missed one a while back. The one I told you about what I saw when we were running from Paranor. I could see better than I let on.

Funny thing. I kept seeing Garet Jax... when I should have been seeing you.

Things that aren't real.

You sure about that?

You know how the magic works—it makes people believe they see things that aren't there.

I'm not sure of anything. Not anymore. A part of me was ready to embrace the magic ... to become Garet Jax forever. A part of me wanted that. To be invincible.

But I knew the source. It is a darkness in my own heart whispering to me, an invitation to a bottomless pit, and I knew I shouldn't listen.

But this doesn't end it. What about next time? What if I'm forced to use the magic of the wishsong again?

I can't pretend it won't happen. I can't be sure there won't be a need for it.

And if there is ...

What happens then?

aBOUT THE CREATORS

TERRY BROOKS is the *New York Times* bestselling author of more than twenty-five books, including the Genesis of Shannara novels *Armageddon's Children* and *The Elves of Cintra*; *The Sword of Shannara*; the nonfiction book *Sometimes the Magic Works: Lessons from a Writing Life*; and many more, including *Wishsong of Shannara*, which forms the basis for this graphic novel. His novels *Running with the Demon* and *A Knight of the Word* were selected by the *Rocky Mountain News* as two of the best science fiction/fantasy novels of the twentieth century. The author was a practicing attorney for many years but now writes full-time. He lives with his wife, Judine, in the Pacific Northwest. Visit the world of Shannara online at **www.shannara.com** and at **www.terrybrooks.net**.

ROBERT PLACE NAPTON has been writing comic books and graphic novels since the 1990s; among his titles are *Deity* and *Saint Angel*. His current works include *Battlestar Galactica Origins: Adama*, based on the Sci-Fi Channel television series, and the pirate adventure series *Blackbeard*, both from Dynamite Entertainment, as well as the historical epic *Rostam* from Hyperwerks Comics. His upcoming works include an original graphic novel entitled *Sage: A Fantasy Documentary* and his first prose novel, *Creatures of the Dust*. He lives with his wife, Anna, (and two cats and a turtle) in Pasadena, California.

EDWIN HUANG DAVID is a comic book artist, digital graphic designer, and painter. He has worked with Alex Ross on *Battle of the Planets* for Top Cow and is currently working on an original series titled *ShadowChasers*. Visit his website at **www.edwindavidart.com**.

the making of
dark wraith of shannara

In the Beginning

Dark Wraith of Shannara was the work of many hands over many months. The participants communicated across the distance between two continents, four states, and who knows how many time zones. Yet a shared dedication to bringing this adventure to life resulted in a book that author, adapter, editor, inker, and toner are all proud to call their own.

The book began with a story by Terry Brooks. As Terry describes it:

"The approach to creating the graphic novel was simple. I was to come up with a new story set in the Shannara world centered around the characters from *Wishsong of Shannara*, and Jair Ohmsford in particular. My concerns about having to write and draw the story were quickly resolved. Stick figures and dialogue consisting of exclamations were the limit of my very rudimentary skills, and we all knew that wasn't going to cut it. So writer Robert Napton and artist Edwin David were brought aboard to do the heavy lifting."

Terry's detailed story outline went to adapter Robert Place Napton for the next step. Robert was selected for the project partly because he was a longtime reader of the Shannara stories.

"The first question I get about this project is if I was a fan of Terry's before taking on the assignment, and the answer is absolutely yes: Terry's writing had a big impact on me. So naturally the second question I get is if I was daunted or intimidated to adapt one of his stories, and I have to say honestly the answer is no. There's a statement people use which I always thought was a cliché, and it goes something like 'Everything I've ever done has prepared me for this.' But in all honesty that's how I felt about *Dark Wraith*. I really felt I could bring all my experience as a comic book and graphic novel writer to bear."

Robert had a unique take on the outline provided by Terry Brooks. "I was excited to learn that the story would be a direct sequel to the first Shannara trilogy, focusing on the characters introduced in the novel *Wishsong of Shannara*. I also thought that the story worked perfectly with the form we were planning on using: black, white, and gray art. Terry himself commented once on the influence of the film *The Seven Samurai* on *Wishsong*'s storyline, and that really inspired my own thinking in terms of what *Dark Wraith* should look like—I wanted the art to have that beautiful Kurasawa-inspired black-and-white poetry that explored not only a world but the nature of humanity in that world. To me that's what Kurasawa's work is about, and it's what Terry's work is about. It's about us. The us we would like to be."

Creating the Overall Look

"My first consideration was the chapter breaks Terry had created in the outline," Robert explains. "My first notion was to have no chapter breaks at all—I wanted the story to play out in a more cinematic nature, harking back to *The Seven Samurai* experience I wanted to re-create. But upon reflection, I wanted to honor the story's novelistic roots, so I proposed five chapter breaks where I thought they would make most sense in a graphic novel, and Terry agreed.

"Once that was settled, I began the job of adding the necessary details to springboard *Dark Wraith*'s plot into 160 pages of graphic novel. Terry's outline was dense, rich with detail, and I wished at times I had more than 160 pages to adapt the story. I revisited a manga I hadn't looked at for years, the brilliant classic *Lone Wolf and Cub*, for its astonishing and very Eastern panel pacing. But *Lone Wolf* has twenty-eight volumes of three hundred pages each or some such, so a bit more real estate than we had to play with. You'll notice the inspirations I drew from before the project started were both Eastern and Western, playing to Edwin's strengths as an artist and perfectly matching the theme and feel of Terry's story. With these influences acting upon me, I felt it was important to write the plot by breaking down the shots panel by panel and describing the story and action to Edwin, but leaving the dialogue for later."

Next Step: Artist Edwin David

Edwin David, who lives in the Philippines, relied on the Internet to keep in touch with Robert Napton in California, Terry Brooks in Seattle, and editor Betsy Mitchell in New York City. Bad weather in the Pacific affected communications and sometimes meant a slowdown in the process!

"It was daunting to be able to work with Terry Brooks," Edwin says. "To be given the chance to design the characters was really exhilarating, yet nerve-racking at the same time. But he's a really open-minded guy, and gave support to the designs we gave him." The Croton Witch, just as one example, was a new character to the Shannara world, and Terry gave Edwin carte blanche to bring her to visual life. Edwin's first concept drawings of her were a little too "over the top" for Terry (see Artist's Sketchbook section), but, adds Edwin, "a few adjustments were made and the designs were finally approved.

"As for the level of comfort in our working relationship," Edwin said, "as the book slowly progressed from the early sketches to the layouts, the level of trust grew so that the final layouts could be drawn roughly, as if Mr. Brooks already had a feel for what was going on even without the details."

An example of a very detailed page layout submitted by Edwin early in the process follows.

page 1 layout

And here is an example of the way the later sketches were provided, after Terry, Robert, and Edwin had established a comfortable working relationship.

"Edwin was fantastic at interpreting my panel descriptions and in every case improving upon them with his great artistic and compositional skills," says Robert Napton. "Though I can't draw *at all*, I would sketch my ideas for the panels before I would write out the plot. These sketches were of such quality that my wife referred to them as potato heads, or 'taters' for short, to give you an idea of how well I can draw. Still, as bad as they were, I found it was important to consider the physicality of the panels on a page in order to suggest the best flow of panels and beats for Edwin. Of course, every step of the way, Terry would comment on the plot (the written version, not the taters—I never let those out of the house) and the subsequent page layouts that resulted. I really wanted sweeping wide shots to show the vistas that Terry so vividly describes in the novels. One of the joys of reading Shannara, in my opinion, is the amazing richness of detail and beauty Terry sees in the natural world and how he brings that to life in his prose. I really wanted the shots to convey that same majesty and poetry and respect and affection that I think Terry has for nature.

"The same goes for the action sequences. An amazing passage in *Wishsong* is the description of Allanon's battle to the death—it is the written equivalent of a great film director staging an amazing battle scene. So I took a big cue from that scene, along with a healthy dash of Kurasawa and *Lone Wolf and Cub*, and then tried to give Edwin as many ideas as I could before he'd cut loose and make the action sequences his own with his amazing artwork, taking what I had written to the next level with his great artist's eye. I'll never forget when I got all the early pages from Edwin of the first time Jair becomes Jax and the subsequent battle with the Rets. It was something special.

"Having Terry approve everything every step of the way was a great safety net," Robert concludes. "I knew if we strayed from his vision of Shannara Terry would let us know, and he did. He was our guide and he always urged us to explore ideas, even if they differed from his. Since this is the first-ever Shannara graphic novel, I felt it would be impossible to please all the fans out there, but if we pleased Terry and he gave us the thumbs up, then there was nothing more we needed to do."

The Script

Plot and artwork took almost a year, with inker Dennis Crisostomo and toner Brian Buccellato contributing their work after Edwin David finished the pencils. After all 160 pages of art were completed, Robert Napton began writing the dialogue. For him, Robert says, "This is where I would really get a chance to have some fun—because other than Terry no writer had ever brought these characters to life, and I had the chance to play in his sandbox. A character that really stands out for me is Slanter. I enjoyed finding his voice, and hopefully I brought something a little different to it rather than just emulating the exact rhythm of his character in *Wishsong*. I tried to move everyone a bit forward in time, in terms of personality and temperament. These aren't the exact same characters from *Wishsong* and the novella "Indomitable"—people change and grow, so I tried to reflect that in the characters' attitudes and voices.

"As with the plot, I'd submit the script to Terry and he'd give me notes. There were changes here and there, but Terry approved and encouraged the direction I was taking. The third act presented the biggest challenges. Because the Croton Witch was a brand-new character, her personality wasn't as defined—there wasn't a novel or short story to draw upon for her motivations and persona. I had an idea of her being mute, but then I thought she should talk, but only in a demonic tongue not understandable to the reader. I felt this would make her more mysterious and scary, and Terry agreed with this notion. But because she was undefined, I tried a few ideas that didn't work as well. I had the idea of her being more of a temptress for Jair—trying to lure him into the darkness—but it really didn't fit Terry's vision of the character, so I rewrote these scenes more than any other in the book to strike the right chord for our new villainous Witch. Similarly, Jair's final scene took a few passes, and Terry himself took to the keyboard and did the final pass, ending it on a note that left me, and hopefully the reader, wondering about the future and ready for more."

As the project drew to a close, Terry Brooks had nothing but praise for his collaborators: "Their considerable talents are evident in every panel of the book. My job was to supervise and approve the work, and it turned out to be much easier than I had expected. Both Robert and Edwin knew the Shannara world and pretty much got it right on the first try."

aRtIST's sketchBook

Terry Brooks and Edwin David worked closely to come up with the correct visual representation of each character. Terry's notes to Edwin appear under each concept sketch.

'CROTON WITCH'

TOMO

The Croton Witch, first concept sketch
Terry Brooks: "She's human, so she wouldn't have a tail, or long twisted limbs, or claws. She would be more like a crone. She's cunning, conniving, but not insane. Think Cruella De Ville."

The Croton Witch, revised concept sketch

"ALLANON"

TOMO

Allanon, first concept sketch

Terry Brooks: "Allanon wears a plain, hooded robe, much like a monk's, with no belt or objects hanging off of it. He should not look as menacing as you portray him in this sketch. He can look serious but also somewhat vulnerable."

Allanon, revised sketch

Slanter, first concept sketch

Terry Brooks: "Slanter's cunning is good, but I think he should look a little harder. He is a tough cookie, not an imp."

`SLANTER`

Slanter, revised sketch

Terry Brooks: "Getting closer, but you need to change a few things so that he does not look so much like a dwarf. Gnomes are more lightly built—he should be slimmer, have wiry muscles and no beard. His clothing is fine, and his grumpy attitude comes through well here. He will be about shoulder-height to the human characters in the story."

Slanter, final sketch

penciling, inking, toning

Three talented artists contributed to the final look of *Dark Wraith of Shannara*. Here are two examples of how each page in the book passed through three stages.

GARET JAX, THE WEAPONS MASTER
Pencils by Edwin David

Tones by Brian Buccellato

JAIR OHMSFORD STEALS THE ILDATCH
Pencils by Edwin David

Inks by Dennis Crisostomo

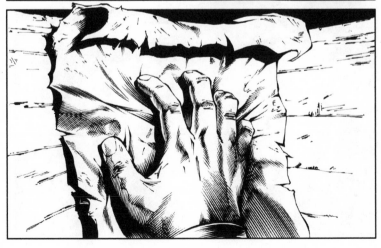

Tones by Brian Buccellato

(Note how the toning process results in a "special effects" feel in the magical glow around the Ildatch.)

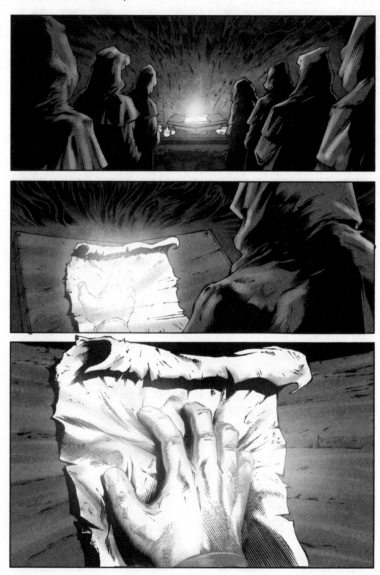